The Spooky Sleepover

'The Spooky Sleepover'
An original concept by Elizabeth Dale
© Elizabeth Dale

Illustrated by Steve Wood

Published by MAVERICK ARTS PUBLISHING LTD
Studio 3A, City Business Centre, 6 Brighton Road,
Horsham, West Sussex, RH13 5BB
© Maverick Arts Publishing Limited March 2019
+44 (0)1403 256941

A CIP catalogue record for this book is available at the British Library.

ISBN 978-1-84886-418-4

www.maverickbooks.co.uk

Gold

This book is rated as: Gold Band (Guided Reading)

The Spooky Sleepover

By **Elizabeth Dale**

Illustrated by **Steve Wood**

Chapter 1

Summer wandered round her new home. How she loved it! It was out in the country, surrounded by fields. It was also big and old and great fun to explore. There was a creaky spiral staircase, narrow corridors and lots of rooms.

She was so excited. She couldn't wait to show her new home to her friends. And they were coming for a sleepover tonight!

"They're here!" her mum cried, as the doorbell rang. Summer rushed to answer it.

"Wow! What a great house!" Gemma cried.

"I'm so excited about our sleepover!" said Marie.

"I'm not sure I've brought enough teddies!" said Ella, peering over a huge pile of them.

Summer laughed. "Come up to my room, and

we'll dump everything there," she said.

Everyone thought Summer's bedroom was brilliant. She had pretty curtains, a big bed and blow-up mattresses on the floor so there was room for them all. Then she showed them round the whole house.

"I like these windows with diamond panes!" said Gemma.

"And look at the sheep outside!" said Marie.

"Yes, and at night you can hear owls!"
Summer said, grinning.

"Are there mice?" asked Ella. "And spiders!
And ghosts?!"

Everyone laughed. And then, as if on cue,
there was a loud wailing sound.

"The ghost!" Ella cried. And everyone squealed.

"What's the matter?" asked Summer's mum, coming in.

"Ella thought she heard a ghost!" Summer said.

"Ah, well," said her mum, smiling. "The last owners did say there's a rumour that the house is haunted..."

Everyone stared at her open-mouthed.

"No way!" Summer gasped.

Her mum laughed. "But they never saw anything – and we all know there's no such thing as ghosts, don't we?"

"Yes!" said Gemma and Marie firmly. But Ella looked worried.

"Don't worry, Ella!" Summer told her. "Come on, let me show you the garden. There's a pond with frogs in it!"

The girls had fun exploring outside. Then they had pizza while watching a movie.

Finally it was bed-time, but no one minded, not when they were having a sleepover.

Chapter 2

As they lay in bed, everyone told each other jokes. Some of them were awful!

And then Summer went out and came back with a tray of nibbles.

"Surprise!" she cried. "This is our Midnight Feast! Mum says it's okay as long as we have it now."

The Midnight Feast was wonderful. Everyone loved it. Afterwards Summer turned off the light. But, everybody was too excited to sleep.

"Let's tell each other ghost stories," said Gemma.

"Oh, yes!" Marie shivered. "I know a really good one!"

She told a story of a bride who was so sad that her bridegroom didn't turn up for their wedding that she threw herself off a tower. And now, as a ghost, she walks along the battlements, carrying her head!

"Oooh!" cried Gemma. "My turn now!"

Her tale was equally spooky. So was Summer's.

"Do you think we should go to sleep now?" asked Ella, nervously.

"Yes, I guess so," said Summer. "Night! Night!"

"Night! Night!" everyone replied.

It was two minutes later that they heard
a scream.

"What was that?" Marie whispered.

"It's the ghost!" Ella cried.

"No," said Summer. "There's no such thing,
remember? It was probably a mouse."

"I've never heard a mouse scream before!"
said Gemma.

"This house is haunted!" wailed Ella.

"It isn't!" said Summer. "Honestly, Ella, I've..." she began.

And then... OooOooOooOooOooW!

The scream was even louder this time.

Ella sat bolt upright. "I'm scared..." she wailed.

Gemma rushed over and put her arm around Ella. "I'm sure it wasn't a ghost," she said.

"I'm never going to get to sleep," Ella moaned.

"In that case," said Summer, getting up and putting on her dressing gown. "Let's go and see just what is making that noise."

"Oh yes!" Marie cried. "Come on!"

Chapter 3

The four friends set off, heading for where the sound had come from.

"Shh!" said Ella. They all stopped and listened. There was silence.

"See!" said Summer. "It was just a mouse and now it's run away."

BONG!

Ella clasped Marie. "What's that?!" she cried.

"Just the clock downstairs!" Summer giggled as they heard more bongs.

"It's midnight!" Marie whispered. "The time when ghosts..."

OooOooOooOooW!

Everyone jumped.
That was very close!
It was coming from right next to them!

Suddenly the lights went out! They all screamed.

"It's okay," said Summer, "this has happened before. It's the wiring in this old house. I'll get a torch. It's good that my mum wears ear-plugs at night. Or we'd have woken her up for sure by now!"

"Or the ghost would..." shuddered Ella as they all followed Summer back to the bedroom.

She quickly found her torch and switched it on. Everyone smiled. And then it went out.

"Oh!" cried Ella. "The ghost did that!"

"No, it just needs new batteries," said Summer. "I'll get them."

Everyone followed her back along the hall.

"They're in one of these cupboards," said Summer, opening a door.

Suddenly something big and white leapt out at her. Summer, Marie and Ella screamed, terrified. But Gemma started laughing.

"Look! It's only a cat!" she said, as it ran down the corridor. "That's what was making that noise!"

As if to prove it, the cat stopped and looked back at them and did a haunting, long M-I-A-O-W!

"That was the sound we heard!" laughed Summer. "I've never seen him before. Poor thing. No wonder he was wailing. He must have jumped inside and then someone shut the door on him."

They all ran after the cat, but he was nowhere to be found.

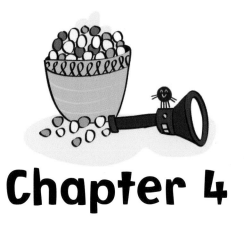

Chapter 4

After that scary experience, the friends huddled up in Summer's bed together. They giggled about how they'd jumped and screamed, and how silly they'd been to think a cat was a ghost! Finally, convinced that there was definitely no ghost, they settled down to sleep.

The next morning, Summer was the first awake. She lay in bed, smiling, as she

thought about the cat. She'd only caught a glimpse but he was so beautiful, with long white fur and one brown ear. Soon the others were awake and they discussed their exciting ghost hunt.

"We should call the cat Midnight, as we saw him just after midnight," said Summer, and everyone agreed.

They all looked for Midnight before they
went down to breakfast but there was no
sign of him. Downstairs, they told Summer's
mum about the white cat with one brown
ear.

"How unusual," Summer's mum said. "I've
never seen him before."

After breakfast, they all searched again for
Midnight, starting outside. When it began

raining, everyone rushed into the house.
They hoped the lovely cat would come in to
keep dry. But they couldn't
find him anywhere.

"What's in here?" asked
Marie pointing to a door
hidden behind a curtain.

"Just a cupboard,
I think," said Summer,
opening a door. But it wasn't, it led into
a small room. Everyone eagerly peered
inside. But there was no cat.

"What a shame," said Summer. But as she
was shutting the door, Ella stopped her.

"Look!" she gasped.

"What?" asked Summer, and then she also gasped. For on the wall was an old portrait of a very elegant-looking lady in a Victorian dress - with a white cat in her arms.

A white cat with one brown ear! Everyone squeezed inside and stared, stunned.

"How many cats can there be just like that?" asked Marie, breathlessly.

"Only one," said Gemma. "It's Midnight!"

"But that painting is really old," said Ella. "And if Midnight was alive then..."

"He must be a ghost now!" everyone cried.

"So the stories about the house being haunted are true," said Marie, "aren't they?!"

"Yes!" Summer cried.

She smiled at her friends. Suddenly the school holidays were about to get a lot more interesting.

"Who wants to come on lots more sleepovers – and ghost hunts?" she asked.

"We do!" her friends cried.

The End

Book Bands for Guided Reading

Pink
Red
Yellow
Blue
Green
Orange
Turquoise
Purple
Gold
White

The Institute of Education book banding system is a scale of colours that reflects the various levels of reading difficulty. The bands are assigned by taking into account the content, the language style, the layout and phonics. Word, phrase and sentence level work is also taken into consideration.

Maverick Early Readers are a bright, attractive range of books covering the pink to white bands. All of these books have been book banded for guided reading to the industry standard and edited by a leading educational consultant.

Cool Duck and Lots of Hats

Catch It, Jess! and Cat Nap

The Space Race

Pirates Don't Drive Diggers

A Right Royal Mess

To view the whole Maverick Readers scheme, visit our website at
www.maverickearlyreaders.com

Or scan the QR code above to view our scheme instantly!